The Bathroom Fact Or Flush Book

———— • ————

by

Russ Edwards

RED-LETTER PRESS, INC.
Saddle River, New Jersey

THE BATHROOM
FACT OR FLUSH BOOK
COPYRIGHT ©2014 Red-Letter Press, Inc.
ISBN-13: 978-1-60387-090-0
ISBN: 1-60387-090-3

Red-Letter Press, Inc.
P.O. Box 393
Saddle River, NJ 07458

www.Red-LetterPress.com

ACKNOWLEDGMENTS

EDITORIAL:
Jack Kreismer

•

BOOK DESIGN & TYPOGRAPHY:
Jeff Kreismer

•

COVER:
Jeff Godby

•

INTERIOR ART:
Andrew Towl

The Bathroom Fact Or Flush Book

Animal Fact or Flush

How much do you know about the creatures that
share our planet? Do you swim with the brainy
dolphins or slither with the slimy slugs?

1. Giraffes have the highest blood pressure in the
animal kingdom.

2. Spots on a leopard indicate its age. One spot
equals approximately one month.

3. The arctic puffin mates only in the dark.

4. The best audio speakers are made from snakeskin
that has been shed and dried naturally in the desert.
These can cost over $15,000 a pair.

5. Birds can not survive in outer space.

6. Of all the strange things we know about the
duck-billed platypus, one of the oddest is that it has
no stomach whatsoever.

7. The idea of the elephant's graveyard is a complete
myth.

8. Everyone knows an octopus has eight arms but it
also has three hearts.

9. First produced by Texas A&M, a "mulekey" is a
cross between a mule and a donkey.

10. There is a species of snail named "Ba humbugi."

Answers

1. Fact. They need it to get blood up that long neck.

2. Flush. Leopard spots are like human fingerprints. Each animal has a unique pattern. The spots, or rosettes, are circular in East Africa but tend to be squarer in southern Africa and, in Asia, the spots are larger.

3. Flush. Mating season is in the spring and they can be huffin' and puffin any time of day. Once mated, puffins usually stay together for life.

4. Flush. A new design made of graphene, a form of carbon, is considered the most responsive.

5. Fact. Their digestive system is dependent on gravity.

6. Fact. It may be hard to swallow but neither does the carp for that matter.

7. Fact. It is well-established legend but not considered true by modern scientists.

8. Fact. Also, octopus arms have their own nervous system and can act independently of the others.

9. Flush. A mule is the offspring of a male donkey and a female horse. A female mule seldom gets pregnant.

10. Fact. It is from Fiji and obviously named by a Dickens fancier. Although "Slimey Tim" may have been the better choice.

Going to the Dogs Fact or Flush

Is it a pedigreed Fact from the Fido File or just another mangy stray that you caught drinking out of the toilet again?

1. The Labrador Retriever was bred in Newfoundland while the Newfoundland dog was bred in Labrador.

2. Three dogs survived the sinking of the Titanic.

3. Puppies are born blind but have perfect hearing.

4. Dogs kick after relieving themselves in a feeble attempt to cover their "business."

5. Stray dogs in Russia sometimes use the subway system to travel to areas that afford more food.

6. Nesbit, a guide dog for the blind, racked up over a million air miles and had his own frequent flyer card.

7. The dog that played Lassie on TV was fired from her contract at the studio after bearing a litter of puppies and being unavailable for three months while nursing them.

8. Hyenas are a type of wild dog.

9. Dogs can suffer from a malodorous condition known as "Frito Feet."

10. Rock Star Ozzy Osborne, never considered a major force in the animal rights movement, nonetheless engaged in hand-to-paw combat with a coyote to save the life of his wife's Pomeranian.

Answers

1. Fact.

2. Fact. All were small and traveling first class of course.

3. Flush. They are born deaf as well as blind.

4. Flush. They are using their scent glands to mark their territory.

5. Fact. According to Russian scientists, the canines actually commute, going to plentiful food areas in the day and returning to their homes at night!

6. Fact.

7. Flush. Lassies were male dogs anyway and didn't require maternity leave.

8. Flush. They are actually more closely related to cats.

9. Fact. The doggy equivalent of B.O., it is caused by the bacteria picked up by the paws reacting with the perspiration dogs release through their pads. It can also smell a bit like popcorn.

10. Fact.

Truths of the Throne

For people who need to know where to go, Toiletfinder.com locates the best public restrooms nearby. Their slogan is "May the Flush be with you!"

Find The Flush Factor

The quiz that gives you a "heads up,"
The Flush Factor is a count of how many
false trivia items you'll find below. See if you
can spot the quartet of phony falsehoods
among the facts.

1. The lava lamp was inspired by an egg timer.

2. Elephants are anatomically incapable of turning their heads side to side.

3. CBS TV stands for Combined Broadcast Service.

4. A common weather condition in Hawaii is vog, a combination of fog and gasses from a volcanic eruption.

5. Chesapeake Bay was formed from a meteor impact crater.

6. The Donkey Kong video game was originally intended to feature Popeye the Sailor.

7. A goat's horns are actually long teeth that grow up instead of down.

8. The mustachioed Pringles can guy is named "Peter."

9. If Charles Lindbergh's grandfather hadn't changed the family's last name, the famed aviator would have been known as Charles Manson.

10. The first season of "The Jetsons" premiered in 1962. Work on the second season didn't begin until 1984.

Answers

1. Fact. The psychedelic icon of the Sixties was invented by British accountant Edward Craven-Walker in 1963 after he was inspired by an egg timer he saw in a pub.

2. Flush. They have a similar range of motion as humans.

3. Flush. CBS started as a radio network, The Columbia Broadcasting System.

4. Fact. It is particularly severe on the Kona Coast.

5. Fact. The area that is now so beautiful and lush with wildlife started with a really bad day about 35 million years ago.

6. Fact. The Nintendo folks couldn't get the rights so they took the Popeye, Bluto and Olive Oyl love triangle and turned it into Donkey Kong, so named because its inventor thought "donkey" meant stupid in English.

7. Flush. Whoever heard of brushing your horns after every meal?

8. Flush. The guy with the chips on his shoulder is named Julius.

9. Fact.

10. Fact. 22 years later, they brought back the original cast.

Science Fact or Flush

Did you pay attention in class or did you get your
science education by watching cheesy sci-fi movies on TV?
Let's find out...

1. The Richter Scale, as a way of measuring
earthquakes, was more or less scrapped in the 1970s.

2. There are nine planets in the solar system.

3. Forget about gold. The most expensive substance
on earth is antimatter.

4. Bill Nye The Science Guy was a student of Carl
Sagan's.

5. Diamond is the hardest substance on earth.

6. Albert Einstein detested science fiction.

7. Moon rocks explode on contact with water.

8. A fruit salad tree can grow up to six varieties of
fruit.

9. The lead in pencils is poisonous and people who
have the habit of putting the point to their mouth
should switch to a pen.

10. Sir Isaac Newton predicted the world will come to
an end in 2021.

Answers

1. Fact. It was replaced by the Moment Magnitude Scale, which is used for all large earthquakes by the United States Geological Service.

2. Flush. What planet have you been on? Pluto is no longer considered a planet.

3. Fact. Because of the immense power used in making it, current prices hover around $62.5 trillion a gram.

4. Fact. Sagan was one of Nye's professors at Cornell.

5. Flush. Actually, it is considered to be the mineral Lonsdaleite. It forms when meteorites containing graphite strike the ground.

6. Fact. He recommended complete abstinence from it, saying, "I never think of the future. It comes soon enough."

7. Flush. They do, however, get soggy.

8. Fact. There are different types but the citrus variety can grow lemons, oranges, limes, grapefruits, tangelos and mandarin.

9. Flush. There is no lead in pencils. It is graphite; but you still shouldn't put the tip in your mouth because it could poke a hole in your...well, you get the point.

10. Flush. Actually the famed scientist said the world will end in 2060 so relax, you still have plenty of time.

Travel Fact or Flush

Are you going places or just totally lost? Prepare for
a journey. Will it be to the known or the unknown?

1. There is a hidden bar in New York City that is only
accessible through a phone booth.

2. The Liberty Bell that they've been displaying in
Philadelphia since 1927 is a replica. The original
cracked, first completely in half and then corroded to
dust in the smoggy city air.

3. Even though it is an immense nation, China has but
a single time zone.

4. There are more barrels of bourbon in Kentucky than
there are people.

5. Eighty-five percent of the land in Nevada is owned
by Uncle Sam.

6. Korea has a national fear of electric fans.

7. The London Underground subway system tunnels
were originally built as bomb shelters during the Blitz.

8. Japan has a longer coastline than Australia.

9. As a safety measure, most airlines require the pilots
to eat different meals.

10. In order to travel in Russia, they now take a DNA
sample along with your passport.

Answers

1. Fact. It used to be a good disguise but nowadays phone booths are so rare it's like having a neon sign out front.

2. Flush. It is still the good old original defective bell and all it's cracked up to be.

3. Fact. All of China is on Beijing time. It doesn't really matter. With all the air pollution, you can't tell if it is day or night anyway.

4. Fact.

5. Fact.

6. Fact. According to the Korea Consumer Protection Board and even most medical authorities, fans are dangerous, especially so in a closed bedroom.

7. Flush. The first section completed was the world's first underground railway and opened in 1863.

8. Fact. Japan has the longer coastline at 29,751 kilometers compared to Australia's 25,760. The country with the longest coastline is Canada, sporting a whopping 202,080 kilometers of coast out of only 356,000 kilometers of coastlines in the entire world.

9. Fact. If they really wanted to be safe, nobody would eat airline food!

10. Flush. Hope we didn't give them any ideas.

Under The Sea Fact or Flush

Will it go swimmingly or will you get in over your head?

1. There are estimated to be around 3 million shipwrecks scattered across the world's oceans.

2. Lobsters were so plentiful in colonial America, they were fed to prisoners.

3. Snoozing seaside sunbathers have been put in the hospital after being attacked by a horde of rogue horseshoe crabs.

4. The East Coast of the United States could sustain heavy damage when an undersea landslide in the Canary Islands eventually lets go.

5. Because of seafloor spreading, Europe moves about an inch further from the US every year.

6. Divers who've come too close to a blue whale have gotten sucked into its blowhole.

7. Undersea communication cables now connect every continent but Antarctica.

8. Dolphins have a form of x-ray vision and can see inside you.

9. In terms of the legal jurisdiction of the United States, 50% of the country lies underwater.

10. Whales not only dive to feed but also to "go the bathroom." It helps keep the waste away from the rest of the pod.

Answers

1. Fact. Although most of these are thought to be pre-historic.

2. Fact. They were regarded as an unpleasant fare.

3. Flush.

4. Fact. It is possible if La Palma collapses due to a volcanic eruption. But don't sell your beachfront property and put your money into buying the movie rights just yet. It could take thousands of years.

5. Fact. No wonder airline fares are going up!

6. Flush. The blowhole is way too small and is opened only above water anyway.

7. Fact. They carry virtually all the Internet traffic between the nations of the world.

8. Fact. Their "sonar" is perfect for penetrating soft tissue. You have no secrets from a dolphin- maybe that's why they always seem to be grinning!

9. Fact. That includes ocean territories.

10. Flush. Where's a 100 ton whale go the bathroom? Anywhere it wants.

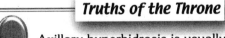

Truths of the Throne

Axillary hyperhidrosis is usually treated in the bathroom - that's what your antiperspirant is for.

Food Fact or Flush

Are you hungry for more?
Well here's some food for thought.

1. Coca Cola originally contained cocaine.

2. When Taco Bell went into the Mexican market, they promoted their menu as "Authentic American Food."

3. Drinking too much carrot juice can turn someone orange.

4. Peanuts are often used as an ingredient in dynamite.

5. What we call "pumpkins" didn't exist before 1907, when botanists at the University of Iowa succeeded in crossing a spaghetti squash with a butternut squash.

6. In the 1930s, there was a popular brand of pancake batter called "Flipjacks" which contained 20% popcorn so that when the pancakes were cooked, they flipped themselves.

7. Bananas are radioactive.

8. One-third of Americans get 47% of their calories from eating junk food.

9. German chocolate, as in German Chocolate Cake, is named after Sam German.

10. Originally, the Big Mac was called the "Aristocrat" but that name was considered "too difficult" for the customers.

Answers

1. Fact. Although it was only ever a tiny amount, Coca Cola went entirely cocaine-free in 1929.

2. Fact. They were not overly successful.

3. Fact. If you have a light complexion, too much carrot juice can give you an orange or yellow tinge- if you drink a LOT of carrot juice.

4. Fact. They are used in the glycerol part of the dynamite's nitroglycerine. Coconuts and soybeans can also be used.

5. Flush. Around for thousands of years, pumpkins grow naturally on every continent but Antarctica.

6. Flush. But that was an old joke that goes back at least to the 1930s.

7. Fact. They contain potassium, a certain percentage of which undergoes radioactive decay. Still, you'd need to eat about 200 to get the same radiation dosage as one chest x-ray.

8. Fact. And many probably get the remaining 53% from washing the junk food down with soda pop.

9. Fact. Sam created it while working at The Baker's Chocolate Company in the mid-1850s.

10. Fact. First made in a Pittsburgh McDonalds owned by Jim Delligatti, the next name tried was "Blue Ribbon Burger." Finally, Esther Glickstein Rose, an advertising secretary at the company headquarters near Chicago, coined the name Big Mac.

All Over the Map Fact or Flush

Know before you go. Is it a roadside
attraction or just a distraction?

1. A popular Virginia tourist attraction, "Foamhenge,"
is like Stonehenge but made out of Styrofoam.

2. All Information-Superhighways lead to Rome,
Georgia, and to a monument marking the spot where
the Internet began in a long-gone government building.

3. Off a desolate stretch of Route 50 in the rippling
heat of the Nevada desert, there's a cottonwood tree
festooned with thousands of pairs of shoes.

4. Snake City, Wyoming, boasts "The biggest
collection of snakes outside Washington D.C." They
hold snake races and an annual "Rattler Round-Up."

5. The main attraction in Gays, Illinois, is the nation's
only two-story outhouse.

6. "The World's Largest Ball of Twine" can be found
in Cawker City, Kansas.

7. One of Maine's popular attractions is a desert.

8. "The World's Biggest Noodle" is housed in a
humidity controlled airplane hanger in Tillamook,
Oregon. This massive walk-through rigatoni required
100 tons of semolina flour to build.

9. There are several "Pizza Farms" in the United States
that consist of round plots of land, divided into slices,
each of which grow particular pizza ingredients.

10. The "World's Largest Office Chair" fills a vacant
lot in Anniston, Alabama.

Answers

1. Fact. It probably looks pretty cool in a hurricane.

2. Flush.

3. Fact. Beginning in the 1980s, thousands of tourists have tossed their footwear into "The Shoe Tree."

4. Flush.

5. Fact. And here's a tip: If you plan to go there, call ahead and try to reserve the upper story!

6. Flush. That's the second-largest ball of twine. The biggest ball's location depends on how you size them up. Branson, Missouri, is the official record holder at 41.5 feet in diameter but it is plastic and therefore lighter. Lake Nebagamon, Wisconsin, claims the heaviest at almost 10 tons.

7. Fact. If not technically, at least in name, "The Desert of Maine" is a 40-plus acre area of rolling sand dunes that resulted from poor land use in the 19th century. Opened in 1925, it has been popular ever since.

8. Flush.

9. Fact. The largest of these educational farms is in Fresno, California. That's a real "pizza" trivia for you.

10. Fact. A 33 foot tall office chair marks the location of Miller's Hardware. Wonder if it serves as the county seat?

Supermarket Sweep Fact or Flush

Feel free to squeeze, pinch and otherwise inspect
the following items and separate the fresh facts
from the overripe rubbish.

1. Philadelphia brand cream cheese was created and
first produced in The City of Brotherly Love.

2. Pistachios were dyed red because of their cost.
Parents didn't want kids sneaking the valuable treat.
With the dye, they'd be caught red-handed.

3. Lettuce is a member of the sunflower family.

4. The shape of a Pringles chip is called a hyperbolic
paraboloid.

5. "Betty Crocker" is just a name the company cooked
up in 1921.

6. Cap'n Crunch leads his hearty crew aboard the
good ship Leakin' Lena.

7. Pound cake got its name from the original recipe,
which called for a pound each of butter, sugar, eggs
and flour.

8. The first grocery coupon ever issued was for Post's
Grape Nuts.

9. Saltines are covered with holes to help catch the
tiny salt crystals that give them their name.

10. And after all this food, what could be more natural
than Pepto-Bismol? This Swiss Army Knife of stomach
ailments was originally developed in the 1940s to quell
runaway nuclear reactions.

Answers

1. Flush. Several businessmen from Chester, NY, created and sold the cheese in the late 1800s. It had nothing to do with Philadelphia.

2. Flush. They were grown in the Middle East and processing equipment marred the shells so they were dyed to cover the imperfections. Nowadays, the nuts are mostly grown in California.

3. Fact. It is also related to asters.

4. Fact. The shape helps keep the chips from breaking while stacked in the can.

5. Fact. Just like Mrs. Butterworth and Aunt Jemima, Betty Crocker is a marketing creation- "Betty" because it sounded friendly and "Crocker" because it was the name of someone on the board of directors.

6. Flush. The Cap'n commands the S. S. Guppy.

7. Fact.

8. Fact. C.W. Post, the breakfast cereal magnate, introduced the idea of coupons in 1895 when he offered a one-cent discount to kick off his new product, a bestseller to this day.

9. Flush. The holes are there to allow air bubbles to escape while they are baked.

10. Flush. It was invented in 1901 as a remedy for infant diarrhea although today it is used primarily for adults. It is also used nowadays to help birds recover from oil spills.

Flush Out The False Fact

Each question has two truths and
a faux fact- flush it out!

1. Former CBS newsman Walter Cronkite, ABC's
George Stephanopolous and NBC anchor Brian
Williams were all college dropouts.

2. Abe Lincoln is related to Tom Hanks, was a licensed
bartender, and a magician.

3. Alfred Hitchcock never won a Best Director Oscar,
Stephen Hawking has never won a Nobel Prize, and
Johnny Carson never won an Emmy.

4. Ben Franklin coined the words "battery," "voltage,"
and "charge."

5. There is an official Wear Your Pajamas To Work
Day, Star Wars Day, and Buy New Underwear Day.

6. The full moon in March is The Worm Moon, the full
moon of May is The Flower Moon, and the full moon
of July is The Liberty Moon.

7. A normal cat has 18 toes, a bowling lane is 60 feet
long, and a quarter has 225 ridges around its edge.

8. Owls are unable to move their eyelids, elephants
can't jump, and dolphins can't hear underwater.

9. Mr. Clean has a first name, Snap! Crackle! and
Pop! are called Pif! Pof! Paf! in Italy, and the
Coppertone Girl is named Sunny.

10. "A" is the most commonly used letter in English,
"the" is the most commonly used word, and the word
"set" has the most definitions.

Answers

1. George Stephanopoulos *did* graduate from college. Cronkite and Williams did not.

2. A magician he was not.

3. Johnny Carson won many awards, including Emmys.

4. He did not coin the word "voltage," but did coin the electrical terms "positive" and "negative".

5. The 18th of April celebrates wearing pajamas, and "Star Wars Day" is May the fourth (be with you). As far as the underwear thing, you're on your own.

6. July skies are decorated with "The Buck Moon," sometimes called "The Thunder Moon" or "The Hay Moon."

7. A quarter has 119 ridges, not 225.

8. Dolphins *can* hear underwater, sounds as far as 15 miles away.

9. Little Miss Coppertone has no official name. By the way, Mr. Clean's first name is Veritably.

10. "E" is the most commonly used letter, not "A."

Truths of the Throne

27,000 trees are wiped out every day to produce toilet paper.

Strictly Business Fact or Flush

How's your business sense? Doesn't matter.
What counts here is native guile, an ability to sense
when someone is trying to bamboozle you.

1. During the recent financial crash, banks offered large bonuses to depositors not to close their accounts. Bank of America paid out over $20 billion alone.

2. Auto manufacturers are gearing up for the day in the not-too-distant future when they will be required to include airbags on the outside of the car as well.

3. In the USA, the soft drink Dr Pepper is bottled by both Coke and Pepsi.

4. The ambulance business in the US is bigger than the movie business.

5. Brooks Brothers has dressed every American president since Lincoln.

6. In the 1950s, the missiles used to launch nuclear warheads were made by Chrysler.

7. Mazda built their auto company by offering a Wankle with every car.

8. Every minute in the United States a person is cheated out of $10,000 or more by one of those Nigerian Prince email schemes.

9. In the 1950s, in an effort to cut down on the unhealthy effects of tobacco, a major company outfitted their cigarettes with filters made of asbestos.

10. The name "Yahoo" came about as a Japanese misspelling of "Yoo Hoo", a name meant to call attention to the new web search service.

Answers

1. Flush. Just like what the financial sector did with your money.

2. Fact.

3. Fact. Don't ask. It's complicated.

4. Fact. The ambulance industry takes in more than the film industry. On the other hand, the movie business sells a lot more popcorn.

5. Fact. They are the oldest men's clothier in the nation.

6. Fact. And if they said "Dodge" on the side, you'd better do it!

7. Fact. The Wankle was a rotary engine. It was simple and smooth but had terrible fuel economy.

8. Flush. By this time most people are wise.

9. Fact. Between 1952 and 1956, about 12 billion Kent cigarettes were sold with asbestos-laden "Micronite" filters. Today's micronite filters have no asbestos but on the other hand, they are still attached to tobacco.

10. Flush. It stands for "Yet Another Hierarchical Officious Oracle."

Build A Better Mousetrap
Fact or Flush

Another assortment of inventors, inventions
and patently ridiculous statements...

1. The first "Teddy Bear" was inspired by the pandas
the designer saw on a trip to China.

2. Bubble gum was invented in 1887 as a caulking
for wooden ship hulls.

3. The alarm clock was invented by Plato.

4. Hawaiian Punch was originally invented as a tropical
flavored topping for ice cream.

5. Sonny Bono scored his first major success by
inventing the game of "Twister" in 1960.

6. A smoke detector has been invented that emits
wasabi vapor when it detects a fire.

7. Polytetrafluoroethylene is the most powerful
chemical explosive ever invented.

8. Old time Hollywood actress Hedy Lamarr invented
the technology that makes Bluetooth possible.

9. The word "Hello" is another one on Thomas
Edison's long list of inventions.

10. Bagpipes were invented in Persia rather than
Scotland.

Answers

1. Flush. It was inspired by a bear cub tied to a tree that Teddy Roosevelt refused to shoot because it wouldn't be sporting or fair.

2. Flush. Although many attempts were made to invent a gum that could blow bubbles, it was Walter Diemer who perfected it in 1928.

3. Fact. He added a whistle to an already existing water clock so that his students would wake up and attend his classes on time.

4. Fact. A.W. Leo, Tom Yates and Ralph Harrison created it as a topping but later discovered adding water made it a great drink.

5. Flush. "Twister" was patented in 1966 by Charles F. Foley and Neil Rabens and given its first big sales boost when Johnny Carson played it with Eva Gabor on "The Tonight Show."

6. Fact. Created for deaf people, research shows they wake up within 10 seconds of smelling the wasabi.

7. Flush. This one was slippery- It's Teflon.

8. Fact. Her frequency-hopping invention is also the basis for Wi-Fi and many other communication technologies.

9. Fact. The new word won out over Alexander Graham Bell's preferred telephone greeting, "Ahoy!"

10. Fact. It eventually spread to Scotland and was popularized there.

Pot Luck
Fact or Flush

1. The only position not mentioned in Abbott and Costello's "Who's on First?" routine is right field.

2. Pope Francis worked as a bouncer in a Buenos Aires bar.

3. Clarence Crane invented the rubber raft in 1912, the same year the Titanic sunk.

4. The giraffe is the only animal born with horns.

5. The CIA has its own college. Good ole CIAU.

6. The Leaning Tower of Pisa has the same amount of stories as there are slices in a standard pizza pie.

7. Q-Tips were originally called C-Tips.

8. Eric Marlon Bishop is better known as Tom Cruise.

9. First deployed in the 1950s, B-52s are scheduled to be in service until the 2040s.

10. Ronald Reagan is the only US president in history ever to be caught dressed up like a Nazi.

Answers

1. Fact.

2. Fact. He also worked as a janitor to help pay for his studies.

3. Flush. Ironically, Crane, who was a candymaker, did introduce Life Savers that year.

4. Fact.

5. Fact. Wonder if you can earn a BA- Best Assassin? Or maybe go for an MS- Master Spy?

6. Fact. (8)

7. Flush. They were first called "Baby Gays."

8. Flush. He's Jamie Foxx.

9. Fact. They've been upgraded continuously since 1955.

10. Fact. In the 1942 movie, "Desperate Journey," Reagan played an American army officer disguised as a Nazi.

Truths of the Throne

What do Elvis, Orville Redenbacher, Jim Morrison and Lenny Bruce have in common? They all went into the bathroom and never came out.

Find The Flush Factor

Plumb the following statements and plug the leaks by finding the four that don't hold water…

1. A solar eclipse can only happen when the moon is full.

2. As a life form, spiders are older than dinosaurs.

3. Before finding international fame as James Bond, Sean Connery worked as a coffin polisher.

4. A jack-in-the-box that has popped open will weigh slightly less than an identical one that is closed.

5. During NASA's Gemini program, one ingredient of the Atlas launch vehicle's rocket fuel was cranberry juice.

6. April 25th is National Zucchini Bread Day.

7. "Ghostbusters" original title was "Ghost Wranglers."

8. Stefani Joanne Angelina Germanotta is now better known as Lady Gaga.

9. Al Gore and Al Franken were once roomies at Harvard.

10. Those expensive Hawaiian favorites, macadamia nuts, are highly toxic to dogs.

Answers

1. Flush. A solar eclipse only occurs when there's a new moon, which is the opposite of a full moon.

2. Fact. Spiders developed over 300 million years ago- so the next time you find one stuck in your bathtub or sink, show some respect.

3. Fact. He also worked as a milkman. Wonder if he had a "License to spill"?

4. Fact. Spring tension is energy and energy has weight.

5. Flush. The cranberries would have "bogged" it down.

6. Fact. And if you think that sounds half-baked, consider that June 16th is National Vinegar Day and July 3rd is National Eat Beans Day, so don't assume every "boom" you hear on the Fourth is from fireworks.

7. Flush. Actually the original title was "Ghost Smashers."

8. Fact.

9. Flush. Al Gore's roomie was Tommy Lee Jones. The unlikely pair were the inspiration for the character of Oliver in "Love Story," written by Erich Segal, another Harvard alum.

10. Fact. And if they're chocolate covered, it is even worse. Grapes and raisins are also bad for Fido.

Here, There and Everywhere
Fact or Flush

An around the world fact or flush finding mission...

1. In Fiji, punishment for most petty crimes up to and including burglary is the revocation of your surfing or boating rights for one year.

2. In the "lower 48" states, Seattle is the city with the longest amount of sunlight in a day.

3. Carson City, Nevada, doesn't observe Halloween on October 31st.

4. In much of Europe, dandelions are considered a delicacy.

5. Many third world countries have classes which teach "Beggar English." The two-day course promises to teach locals enough to get by when targeting American tourists.

6. The third largest business in Ecuador is llama rental.

7. The legendary "Tin Pan Alley" that gave the world so many great songs before the rock and roll era is a part of lower Broadway in New York City.

8. Russia's largest and most important export is free.

9. The longest commercial flight in the world is from Sydney, Australia, to Dallas, Texas.

10. In France, you can get married even if you've gone to that Big Singles Bar In The Sky. (Yes, even after you are deceased.)

Answers

1. Flush. Of course, you can't surf or boat in prison.

2. Fact. A day can have 16 hours of sunlight compared to Miami's 13 hours, 48 minutes or New York's 15 hours, 8 minutes.

3. Fact. That's reserved for Nevada Day. Halloween happens on October 30th.

4. Fact. What we consider a weed, they use in salads, wines and other recipes.

5. Flush. Besides, being poor and desperate is a universal language.

6. Flush. Oil, bananas and cocoa are all major industries.

7. Flush. It was West 28th street between 5th and 6th Avenues in Manhattan.

8. Fact. It produces more oxygen than any other country in the world.

9. Fact. It takes about 16 hours. It's certainly no flight on which to get into a game of "peek-a-boo" with a baby.

10. Fact. It happens a couple of dozen times a year but admittedly takes the fun out of the honeymoon.

Credible or Incredible Fact or Flush

Another potpourri of pronouncements to ponder...

1. Alaska is the northernmost, westernmost and easternmost state in the union.

2. Kiefer Sutherland once put his acting career on hold to become a rodeo star.

3. Ben & Jerry's ice cream exists because the equipment to make bagels was too expensive.

4. SETI, or the Search for Extraterrestrial Intelligence, continually beams a signal into deep space inviting aliens to land in San Francisco's Golden Gate Park.

5. Barzman's Frog, a large amphibian in Indonesia, perfectly imitates bird mating calls in order to attract its prey. It can even camouflage itself as an egg in a nest.

6. The last time a Republican was elected President without a Nixon or Bush on the ticket was Herbert Hoover in 1928.

7. A Connecticut cat named Lewis was once sentenced to house arrest for attacking an Avon lady.

8. The treadmills on the International Space Station are named after Stephen Colbert.

9. At the annual "Higher Than A Kite" kite festival in Venice Beach, California, participants are required to be legally drunk.

10. There is no word that rhymes with "orange".

Answers

1. Fact. Northernmost and westernmost are obvious but as the Aleutian Islands reach across the International Date Line, it is also the easternmost.

2. Fact. He won several prizes in roping events.

3. Fact. The pair wanted to go into the bagel business but didn't have the dough.

4. Flush. As well as they might fit in there, the invitation has not been formally sent.

5. Flush.

6. Fact.

7. Fact. To be fair, the cat had no choice. It was holding a Tupperware Party at the time.

8. Fact. They are called "Combined Operational Load-Bearing External Resistance Treadmills," an acronym for Colbert.

9. Flush. But now that the idea's out there, any town looking to boost tourism might want to look into it.

10. Flush. "Sporange" is a botanical term for spore case.

Truths of the Throne

You can open many airline lavatories by looking behind the "No Smoking" sign and sliding the bolt over. The publisher is not responsible for what happens next.

Blasts From the Past Fact or Flush

The old admonition, "Don't believe everything you read," certainly applies here, but there are also some surprising actual facts, so don't rush to flush.

1. By the time of the battle of Gettysburg, U.S. Grant owned slaves, Robert E. Lee did not.

2. Davy Crockett once helped save President Andrew Jackson from an assassin.

3. Public screenings of projected motion pictures were invented at the end of 1895. A year later porn flicks were introduced.

4. Before alarm clocks were widely available in the 1920s, people would engage a "knocker-up" to wake them by a certain time.

5. In 1886, New York City's first ticker tape parade honored sharpshooter Annie Oakley.

6. Santa Catalina Island in California was once owned by chewing gum magnate William Wrigley Jr.

7. The original home of the NFL's Washington Redskins, whose nickname has created controversy, was in the land of the Patriots, Boston, Massachusetts.

8. President Millard Fillmore had the first White House bathtub installed in 1850.

9. Karl Marx (of Communism fame) was once a correspondent for "The New York Daily Tribune."

10. The presidential proclamation that declared National Harbor Day contained a misprint, so we now celebrate National Arbor Day instead.

Answers

1. Fact. Lee's slaves belonged to his father-in-law. He freed them when he passed away in 1862, believing that slavery was evil. Grant held slaves until 1865.

2. Fact. But by the time he got there, Old Hickory had things well in hand. Crockett subdued the gunman while Jackson continued beating him with his cane.

3. Fact.

4. Fact.

5. Flush. It was, in fact, in honor of The Statue of Liberty.

6. Fact. Realizing the possibilities, he bought the island. The Chicago Cubs, also owned by Wrigley, once used the island for spring training.

7. Fact. The Redskins began play in Boston in 1932 and moved five years later to Washington, D.C.

8. Flush. Although widely quoted in trivia books, the story was a hoax perpetrated by H.L. Mencken in 1917. The first real tub was probably installed during Andrew Jackson's term in 1834.

9. Fact. Horace Greeley's paper hired Marx as a London-based reporter in 1852.

10. Flush. Arbor Day is an international observance. The first American Arbor Day was held in Nebraska City, Nebraska, by J. Sterling Morton.

Fact or Flush Flashback-The Sixties

Far out, funky and fabulous, the Sixties had it going on.
Like, is it groovy or totally bogus, man?

1. JFK nicknamed his favorite rocking chair "Marilyn."

2. The ten years of the 1970s were shorter than the ten years of the 1960s.

3. Peter Sellers was the first man ever to appear on the cover of "Playboy".

4. The Beatles first American television appearance was on "The Ed Sullivan Show" in 1964.

5. Telstar, the much-hyped communications satellite, harbinger of the future and inspiration of a popular instrumental, was essentially shot out of the sky by American and Soviet high altitude nuclear blasts.

6. It was at Woodstock, NY, where three days of "Peace and Music" drew hundreds of thousands of hippies to the music festival in the summer of 1969.

7. Unlike everything else in the 1960s, toilet paper was very drab and only available in white.

8. To reward his biggest contributors, Richard Nixon planned to hold his 1969 inaugural ball at Walt Disney World in Florida. However, the Secret Service felt that he couldn't be protected adequately there.

9. Action figure G.I. Joe, who debuted in 1960, had to get with the times and by the late 1960s was no longer military but an adventurer.

10. The first words spoken on the Moon were "The Eagle has landed."

Answers

1. Flush. He'd have been off his rocker if he had tried to get away with that.

2. Fact. The 1970s didn't have as many leap years.

3. Fact. That push-up bra must have been murder!

4. Flush. They had already appeared on NBC news in a story filed by Edwin Newman.

5. Fact. It only lasted a few months before the radiation fried its transistors.

6. Flush. It was actually held at a farm near White Lake, close to Bethel, NY.

7. Flush. How appropriate for a toilet paper question. Toilet paper was far more colorful than it is today. It came in a wide selection of colors to match bathroom color schemes including lavender, pink, light green and purple.

8. Flush. Walt Disney World didn't open until 1971.

9. Fact. By then, anti-war sentiment had reached the marketing mavens at Hasbro.

10. Flush. Although there's much debate, the first words were probably "Contact light," said by Buzz Aldrin.

Celebrity Fact or Flush

Sort through these odd facts about the famous,
flighty and fabulous among us.

1. Elvis Presley's 8th grade music teacher felt that he couldn't carry a tune in a bucket of fried chicken.

2. The clamp which held the atomic bomb to the Enola Gay in history's first nuclear attack was made by one of the Marx brothers.

3. Before establishing herself as a comedian, Melissa McCarthy distinguished herself as an Air Force nurse in Operation Desert Storm.

4. Soap diva Susan Lucci is the daughter of comedy icon Phyllis Diller.

5. Richard Nixon funded his first political campaign with the thousands of dollars he won playing poker in the South Pacific during World War 2.

6. Tiger Woods is a movie buff who has a $5 million dollar collection of film props including the Batmobile and Dorothy's slippers from "The Wizard of Oz."

7. Christopher Walken was once a lion tamer in the circus.

8. Jimmy Fallon temporarily filled in for his ailing sister as an official Avon Lady when he was 15.

9. Natalie Portman has published papers in scientific journals.

10. Seth McFarlane of "Family Guy" fame has had vocal training from the same couple who taught both Frank Sinatra and Barbra Streisand.

Answers

1. Fact. Elvis's musicality had previously been encouraged in school, but a Memphis teacher told him that he had "no aptitude" for singing.

2. Fact. Zeppo Marx left the act early to pursue his engineering talents. Another invention was a wristwatch alarm which monitored the pulse rate of cardiac patients. Perhaps you've also heard of the "Zeppo" lighter?

3. Flush. She was never a nurse- although they do say laughter is the best medicine.

4. Flush. The oft-heard rumor is not true.

5. Fact. He learned poker from fellow naval officer James Stewart and once turned down a dinner invite with Charles Lindbergh to host a poker game.

6. Flush. He collected other things that turned out to be even more expensive.

7. Fact. Walken would put on a big show of cracking the whip but he describes the lion, Sheba, as a "big, nice old dog."

8. Flush. He was too busy re-enacting that week's "Saturday Night Live."

9. Fact. One was titled "Frontal Lobe Activation during Object Permanence: Data from Near-Infrared Spectroscopy."

10. Fact. At the age of 90, vocal coaches Lee and Sally Sweetland were still shaping talent.

Mixed Greens Fact or Flush

If you're not a greenhorn, you should be
able to tell lush from flush...

1. In Brazil, a popular pizza topping is green peas.

2. Greenland is three times the size of Texas.

3. In the original Dr. Seuss book, The Grinch was depicted as blue.

4. The term "greenback" comes from the notes the US issued in 1861 to finance the Civil War.

5. The world's largest salad weighed almost 42,000 pounds and was tossed together in Romania in 2012.

6. The vivid green phosphors from old-fashioned TV picture tubes came from the ground up shells of a tropical green beetle.

7. Chromium gives emeralds their characteristic green color.

8. The only reason Frankenstein's monster is always pictured as being green is that the original Universal film, shot in black and white, was promoted with lurid posters in which the monster was portrayed as green.

9. For those who like to go ballistic on the golf course, there's the Ballistic Driver. Make your golfing buddies green with envy when you press a button and the club head explodes, guaranteeing you 250 yards every time.

10. Comic superhero Green Lantern's real name is Jack Arrow.

Answers

1. Fact. You might say they put the "p" in pizza.

2. Fact. It is the largest island in the world at 840,000 square miles.

3. Flush. In fact he was colorless. He was turned to green by the TV animators.

4. Fact. The Demand notes literally had a green back.

5. Fact. Guess it was a Romaine-nia Salad.

6. Flush.

7. Fact. Oddly enough, chromium also imparts the reddish color to rubies.

8. Fact. There was no reference to green either in the original novel or the film.

9. Fact. They retail for about $1,000.

10. Flush. There have been several Green Lanterns including Alan Scott, Hal Jordan, and Guy Gardner.

Truths of the Throne

The first patent for rolled toilet paper was issued in 1883 to Seth Wheeler of Albany, New York. Before that, toilet paper was sold in flat sheets.

Body of Knowledge
Fact or Flush

*Do you know your body like the back of your
hand or is your head just not in the game?*

1. There are more neural connections in your brain
than there are stars in the Milky Way galaxy.

2. It is impossible to lick your elbow.

3. Doctors call lateral curvature of the upper spine
"Thoratic dissembulation."

4. If you're a normal human, you will likely shed over
one hundred pounds of skin by age 70.

5. Most people would not consider their morning
ablutions complete if they did not tend to their oxters.

6. A fully grown adult has about a third more bones
than an infant.

7. Identical twins have identical fingerprints.

8. Blondes have more fun and they usually have more
hair as well.

9. Every bone in the human body is connected to
some other bone.

10. Euneirophrenia is the sweaty and panicky state
that you feel upon waking up from a nightmare.

Answers

1. Fact. The connections number in the trillions whereas the stars number only 100 billion or so.

2. Flush. Difficult for most, not impossible for all.

3. Flush. It is known as scoliosis.

4. Fact. You lose about 600,000 skin particles every hour or about 5,000 while you've been reading this question. Please brush the page before continuing.

5. Fact. Oxter is another name for "armpit."

6. Flush. Actually it is exactly the opposite. A baby has 270 bones, an adult, 206.

7. Flush.

8. Fact. Blondes average 146,000 hair follicles while redheads have the fewest at 86,000.

9. Flush. It's almost fact but for the exception of the hyoid bone in the neck, involved in speaking, anchoring the tongue and swallowing.

10. Flush. Just the opposite, it is the warm, calm feeling you get awakening from a pleasant dream.

Invention Fact or Flush

See if the following quiz on inventions makes the light bulb go on over your head or just leaves you in the dark...

1. The true inventor of the fire hydrant cannot be confirmed because the building that stored the patent burned down.

2. The inventor of the Richter Scale, long used to measure earthquake intensity, was a dedicated nudist.

3. Twinkies were first developed as a lightweight, high carb, energy packed space food.

4. Silly String was originally intended as an instant, spray on cast.

5. The classic leg lamp of the holiday perennial "A Christmas Story," was inspired by a soft drink ad.

6. James Franco holds a patent for a car proximity alarm that warns you when you are tailgating.

7. The Internet was invented by Vint Cerf and Bob Kahn back in the 1970s.

8. Karaoke was invented in 1971 by a musician who knew he wouldn't be able to make a gig one night so he recorded the background music in advance.

9. Mark Twain invented a board game called "Mark Twain's Memory Builder."

10. Peanut butter was invented by George Washington Carver.

Answers

1. Fact. But the inventor is generally thought to be Frederick Graff Sr., Chief Engineer of the Philadelphia Water Works circa 1801.

2. Fact. It was odd that Charles Richter felt the need for an earthquake scale. To see how much the ground was swaying, all he had to do was look down.

3. Flush. They were invented in River Forest, Illinois, in 1930, by baker James Alexander Dewar.

4. Fact. Inventors Leonard Fish and Robert Cox discovered by tweaking the formula and adding color, Silly String worked even better as a toy.

5. Fact. Decades ago, a popular soft drink brand was Nehi. To remind consumers that it was pronounced "knee- high," they put out ads featuring shapely legs with stockings up to the knee.

6. Flush. But he did intern at Lockheed Martin.

7. Flush. What is a fact is that the TCP/IP standard which enables data transmission throughout the Internet was invented by Vint Cerf and Bob Kahn while working for the Defense Advanced Research Projects Agency and it is because of their invention you Kahn now Cerf the 'Net.

8. Fact. Daisuke Inoue, a drummer, came up with the idea but never filed a patent.

9. Fact. In 1885, he made one of the first trivia games.

10. Flush. It dates back to the Aztecs in Bolivia.

More Celebrity Fact or Flush

Here's another shot to prove you're
not lame at the fame game.
Can you tell the publicity from the duplicity?

1. Richard Gere has a jewel of a middle name- Tiffany.

2. In his New Jersey youth, Bruce Willis once worked as a numbers runner.

3. Julia Louis-Dreyfus' father is a real-life billionaire.

4. Danica McKellar, best known as Winnie Cooper on "The Wonder Years," is a mathematician and has written several math books for young girls.

5. Hulk Hogan missed the call from his agent that went next to George Foreman asking him to endorse a new grill that was debuting in 1994.

6. Jimmy Kimmel breeds racing pigeons and has won numerous international competitions.

7. Her early career had its ups and down as Madonna once worked as an elevator operator.

8. George Clooney is related to Abe Lincoln.

9. Kate Winslet's mother was the inventor of "Liquid Paper."

10. Paris Hilton once saved a thousand elephants by purchasing them and moving them to a preserve in South Africa.

Answers

1. Fact. It was his mother's maiden name.

2. Flush. He has however run up some nice numbers at the box office.

3. Fact. The star of "Seinfeld" and "Veep" was born with a silver spoon in her mouth but when her mother divorced her father and some years later married the Dean of the George Washington University Medical School, she traded it for a silver tongue depressor.

4. Fact. She studied math at UCLA, graduating summa cum laude.

5. Fact. It has since sold over 100,000,000 units, netting Foreman tens of millions. No one's ever hurt the Hulkster that bad!

6. Flush. However one of Kimmel's frequent guests, Mike Tyson, is into pigeons big time.

7. Fact. She was fired from the job in short order by the way. Forgot the route?

8. Fact. According to Ancestry.com, Lincoln was the half-first cousin five times removed of the movie heartthrob.

9. Flush. It was, in fact, Monkee Mike Nesmith's mom.

10. Flush. If she had, the elephants would certainly have remembered. To be fair, she does do a considerable amount of charity work.

Find The Flush Factor

Ferret out the five phonies
from the five facts…

1. Leslie King grew up to become the
38th President of the US.

2. The first webcam was used to monitor
a bicycle rack.

3. Longtime children's favorite Play Doh was created
as a wallpaper cleaner.

4. Combining his two stints as "Tonight Show" host,
Jay Leno actually held the job longer than Johnny
Carson.

5. Flushes swirl down the toilet in opposite directions
in the Northern and Southern hemispheres.

6. Brian Eno used a Mac computer to create "The
Microsoft Sound" first used in Windows 95.

7. The A&W in the root beer name stands for
company founders Roy Allen and Frank Wright.

8. The Pecktail shark is the only species known that
will attack a nuclear submarine.

9. Playing rock, paper, scissors is also known as
fargling.

10. Ironically, it is impossible to bake angel food cake
above 8,000 feet.

Answers

1. Fact. Leslie King became Gerald Ford when his mother remarried.

2. Flush. It was actually trained on a coffee pot at Cambridge University. Just one of the many perks of college life.

3. Fact. Back then it only came in white.

4. Flush. Johnny's still the champ at 30 seasons. Jay clocked 22 years behind the desk.

5. Flush. This myth has finally gone down the drain once and for all.

6. Fact.

7. Fact. A&W became America's first franchised restaurant chain in 1924, way back before McDonalds was even making McNuggets in its McDiaper.

8. Flush. The Pecktail shark is just a fish story whereas the cookie cutter shark has been known to take bite-sized chunks out of a sub's rubber-coated components.

9. Fact. It is also known as roshambo or ick-ack-ock. A similar but advanced version is known as "Rock, Paper, Scissors, Lizard, Spock" made famous by TV's "Big Bang Theory."

10. Flush. High altitude baking is done differently but nothing specifically rules out angel food cake.

Coast to Coast Fact or Flush

Get your state certification by taking this quiz.

1. New Mexico is the only place in the US with an official state question.

2. Alaska claims over half the total coastline in the United States.

3. New England and the state of Pennsylvania could fit inside the borders of Arizona.

4. Montana claims the largest snowflake on record at nearly 15 inches.

5. It's illegal for a bar or nightclub to hold a "Ladies Night" in California.

6. The Union Jack, the banner of the British Empire, appears as part of Hawaii's flag.

7. Louisiana has the only Governors' Mansion built in the middle of a swamp.

8. Hollywood may be today's film capital but the original dream factory was Fort Lee, New Jersey.

9. The letter "s" is the most common last letter for a state in the US.

10. South Philadelphia is located on a chunk of land New Jersey ceded to Pennsylvania in 1910.

Answers

1. Fact. And the question is…"Red or Green?," referring to your preference for that staple of New Mexico cuisine, the chili pepper.

2. Fact. It has more coastline than all the other states combined.

3. Fact. You have to jam them in a bit but they'd fit.

4. Fact. It fell in 1887 so you kind of had to be there to see it.

5. Fact. It is considered gender discrimination.

6. Fact. It appears where the star field would normally go on the Stars and Stripes.

7. Flush. It's on a beautiful estate in Baton Rouge.

8. Fact. Filmmakers abandoned New Jersey for California because of the dependable weather and to get away from Thomas Edison, who had gained tremendous control over the industry.

9. Flush. The letter "a" is the most common by far. It is the last letter of 21 states.

10. Flush.

Truths of the Throne

It wasn't only the shower scene in "Psycho" that was historic. The film was the first American movie ever to show a toilet flushed on screen.

USA Fact or Flush

Get ready for red, white and blue all-American
"Shock & Awe"- or just plain " Aw Shucks!"

1. Down where the states of Maryland, Pennsylvania, and West Virginia come together, there is rumored to be a crypto-critter known as the Snallygaster.

2. The Deep South is considered to begin at the Mason-Dixon line, which forms the northern border of North Carolina.

3. NASA's Jet Propulsion Laboratory used to hold an official "Miss Guided Missile" beauty pageant.

4. The American toy company Hasbro is the largest distributor of toys in the world.

5. According to Time.com, 11% of Americans think that HTML is a social disease.

6. Alaska is the only US state in which residents drive on the left side of the road as they do in Britain.

7. Hawaii is the only state that doesn't have a straight line anywhere in its border.

8. Grover Cleveland supported himself as a hangman before he became President.

9. There's an official Popcorn Board, established by the US Congress.

10. In order to boost tourism on Route 66, several western states have completely removed speed limits on the fabled road.

Answers

1. Fact. Reported primarily in Maryland, the Snallygaster is reputed to be a winged serpent or dragon which lives in the hills.

2. Flush. For the most part, the Mason-Dixon line forms the southern border of Pennsylvania.

3. Fact. The pageants began in 1952, long before the JPL became part of NASA. Looking back, many people would agree that Miss Guided Missile was simply Miss-Guided.

4. Flush. But another US corporation- McDonalds!- gives Santa a run for his money, distributing 1.5 billion toys annually.

5. Fact. Though, in a sense, while visiting web sites built with it, you might catch a virus.

6. Flush. With all that ice, they drive all over the road.

7. Fact. Even if it had a straight border, waves would play havoc with it.

8. Fact. As the Sheriff of Buffalo, he sometimes had to be Chief Executioner before he became Chief Executive.

9. Fact. Its mission is to "raise awareness of popcorn as a versatile, whole-grain snack."

10. Flush. You can still get your tickets, on Route 66.

Americana Fact or Flush

Discern what's true in the American nation
rather than just in your imagination...

1. Between 1912 and 1959, there were 44 states in the union.

2. The infamous wood chipper from the film "Fargo" is now a popular tourist attraction in North Dakota.

3. Florida has three colors for driver's licenses: Green for those under 25, yellow for those 25-55 and gold for seniors. Each represents different levels of blood alcohol standards in order to be charged with a DUI.

4. The Washington Monument, standing at over 555 feet, is the tallest memorial or monument in America.

5. In Minnesota, it is illegal for a woman to impersonate Santa Claus.

6. Ah, Spring, the season of proms. Romance is in the air... but wait! There's a scent of something else... eleven herbs and spices? That can only mean KFC is selling fried chicken corsages.

7. It is illegal to take more than $5.00 worth of pennies or nickels out of the country.

8. Macy's threw America's first Thanksgiving Day parade back in 1924.

9. "Iron Eyes" Cody, the tearful Native American in the anti-pollution public service ad which ran on TV for decades was, in fact, of Italian-American heritage.

10. King Kong has a star on the Hollywood Walk of Fame.

Answers

1. Fact. We now have 46 states- and four commonwealths: Pennsylvania, Virginia, Massachusetts and Kentucky.

2. Fact.

3. Flush. They can't even count chads. How would they manage that?

4. Flush. The St. Louis Gateway Arch, at 630 feet, holds that honor. It is also the tallest stainless steel monument in the world.

5. Fact. It could be 30 days if you violate the "Santa Clause."

6. Fact. Although there is a danger of them being munched off during slow dancing, it makes KFC a reason that going to a prom is on some people's bucket list.

7. Fact. It could land you in the pokey for up to 5 years. If you break the piggy bank for that big trip to Europe, you best use the change for tips at the airport.

8. Flush. True, Macy's began its holiday parade then, but Gimbel's in Philadelphia originated the tradition in 1920.

9. Fact. He was born Espera DiCorti in Louisiana.

10. Flush. Japanese giant lizard Godzilla does have a star but good old American King Kong does not.

History's Mysteries Fact or Flush

Fun facts and flagrant falsehoods from the pages of history...

1. New York City's mayor was caught up in secession fever in 1861. He wanted to leave the Union and set up the independent republic of Tri-Insula.

2. Jackie Robinson was court martialed from the Army for refusing to give up his seat on a bus.

3. Samoa never experienced December 30th, 2011.

4. Claudia Alta Taylor became First Lady of the United States in the mid 20th Century.

5. Thomas Edison invented FM radio in order to one-up Marconi.

6. During the Energy Crisis of the 1970s, Christmas lights and displays were widely discouraged and even made illegal.

7. Amelia Earhart invented the squeegee to improve the visibility of her airplane's windshield.

8. During the entire administration of Gerald Ford, the Vice-Presidency was vacant.

9. Steve Jobs kept a rock collection from a boyhood trip out West close at hand all his life. It was only after his passing that the rocks were found to be intensely radioactive, probably from a 1950s atomic test.

10. Marilyn Monroe spent World War II building remote-controlled drones aircraft for the war effort.

Answers

1. Fact.

2. Fact. The man who broke Major League Baseball's color barrier was found not guilty and honorably discharged.

3. Fact. At the end of 2011, they switched sides of the International Date Line, so that day never happened.

4. Fact. She was better known as Lady Bird Johnson.

5. Flush. It was developed by Edwin Armstrong, who field-tested it from a lab on the 85th floor of the Empire State Building.

6. Fact.

7. Flush. Italian immigrant Ettore Steccone invented it in Oakland, California, in 1936.

8. Flush. Nelson Rockefeller served in that capacity until 1977.

9. Flush.

10. Fact. She worked at a factory owned by Reginald Denny, the actor who invented them. Denny can be seen as the old Admiral in "Mary Poppins."

Truths of the Throne

Science wanted to know, so taxpayers ponied up $100,000 dollars to determine that three out of four Americans load their toilet paper with the flap in the front.

Presidential Fact or Flush

Review the following factoids about
our Chief Executives down through history
and cast your vote "Yea" or "Nay."

1. Teddy Roosevelt inspired the invention of the forward pass in football.

2. Jimmy Carter is the only president to ever have officially reported seeing a UFO.

3. Before he became president, Richard Nixon invested in Washington D.C.'s Watergate Complex.

4. In 1993, at the tender age of 46, Bill Clinton became our youngest president.

5. The generic dog name "Fido," comes from Abe Lincoln's canine companion.

6. In 1958, JFK's car was rear-ended in Florida with a jalopy driven by Larry King.

7. Eisenhower loved Julia Child's cooking so much that she resided in the White House for six months in 1954 until Ike could find a replacement.

8. Father's Day was established as a permanent national observance by Richard Nixon.

9. Lyndon Johnson was known for holding meetings while he was using the bathroom.

10. More presidents have died on July 4th than on any other single day.

Answers

1. Fact. Without his demand for safer reforms to the game in 1905, today's game wouldn't be the same. Bully and three cheers for Teddy!

2. Fact. He intended to open the secret UFO files to the public after he was elected but was dissuaded due to "security concerns."

3. Flush. That would have been just too ironic.

4. Flush. Roosevelt was 42 and Kennedy was 43.

5. Fact. His presidency popularized the name of his favorite pooch, who was, unfortunately, too undisciplined to live in the White House.

6. Fact. JFK didn't involve police or insurance. He just let King off for his promise to vote for Kennedy for president two years hence.

7. Flush. At the time, she was living in France, working on her book and Ike's tastes ran more to Mamie's Deep Dish Apple Pie, President's Corn Pudding, Mamie's Million Dollar Fudge, Ike's Vegetable Soup and Mamie's Sugar Cookies. They really enjoyed family recipes.

8. Fact. Although Sonora Smart Dodd originated the day in 1910 in Spokane, WA, President Nixon made it permanent and official in 1972.

9. Fact. He was flush with power.

10. Fact. Jefferson, Adams and Monroe all passed into history on Independence Day.

Dictionary or Fictionary

Some of these are real words that you might find
in a dictionary, others, not so much.

1. "Octothorpe" is the name of the pound sign,
number sign or hashtag. Dictionary or Fictionary?

2. "Goombang" is the little ball people used to put
atop their car antenna.

3. "Crow Chute" is the name of the coin return door
slot on pay phones.

4. "Throbber" is the little animated symbol that
appears on your computer screen that indicates that a
program is busy.

5. "Contestosterone" is the supercharged form of the
combined hormones of cortisol and testosterone that
the bodies of trained athletes release just before an
event.

6. "Chu Chu" is how you tell someone to be quiet in
Thai.

7. One of those inexpensive, lightweight, stack-able
plastic chairs you see everywhere, especially on lawns
and porches, is known as a "monobloc" chair.

8. "Umami" is a basic taste like bitter or sweet that has
been described as savory or meaty.

9. A "funambulist" is a tightrope walker.

10. "Nibling" is the gender-neutral term for a niece or
nephew.

Answers

1. Dictionary. The octothorpe has had many uses over the years and many names.

2. Fictionary. Antenna Balls or Toppers first started showing up in the mid-Sixties to advertise Union 76 gas.

3. Fictionary. In the heyday of pay phones, the coin return slot used to be popular with kids to pick up pocket change but in later years, there have been many cases of dangerous objects placed inside.

4. Dictionary. It differs from a progress bar in that it doesn't indicate how much of the process has been completed.

5. Fictionary.

6. Dictionary. By the way, if you ever need to tell a German to hush up, say "Pscht!".

7. Dictionary. It was originally designed by Vico Magistretti in 1967.

8. Dictionary. It's one of the five basic tastes along with sweet, sour, bitter and salty.

9. Dictionary. A funambulist might also be called an equilibrist.

10. Dictionary.

Pot Luck
Fact or Flush

1. A clam which was dredged up off Iceland in 2006 turned out to be 507 years old.

2. It is 120 feet from home plate to second base on a major league baseball diamond.

3. A pound of half-dollars is worth about the same as a pound of dimes or quarters.

4. In times of scarcity, the Gaboon Viper can eat the rear two-thirds of its body.

5. "Q" is the only letter that is not needed to spell the name of any state.

6. Match heads emit significant radiation, thus matchbooks are not recommended to be carried in pockets.

7. Brontology is a subspecialty of paleontology.

8. There is a looming crisis in China. Diners are being asked to forego chopsticks.

9. Charley Douglass is responsible for far more laughs on TV than any other person.

10. The very first host of "Saturday Night Live" was David Brenner.

Answers

1. Fact. "Ming" was born in 1499 as determined by its growth rings.

2. Flush. It's 127 feet, 3 3/8th inches, to be exact.

3. Fact. Around $20.

4. Flush.

5. Fact. It also got snubbed on the phone dial. See what happens when it hangs out with "U" all the time?

6. Flush. Although, smoke detectors do give off radiation, so don't carry them in your pockets either.

7. Flush. It is actually the study of thunder.

8. Fact. The nation has been blowing through 80 billion sets of the disposable implements a year, putting a severe strain on their forests which they desperately need for producing those "Made in China" labels.

9. Fact. He invented the laugh track in the 1950s.

10. Flush. It was George Carlin with musical guest Janis Ian.

Truths of the Throne

The typical person visits the toilet 6 to 8 times a day or 2,500 times a year, spending three years there in an average lifetime.

Historical or Hysterical

As a great man once said, those who haven't learned from
history are doomed to repeatedly peek at the answer page.
Let's find out whether you can tell
historical fact from hysterical hogwash.

1. George Washington was plagued since his early 20s
with wooden teeth. Historical or Hysterical?

2. A very ill Abe Lincoln scrawled the Gettysburg
Address on the back of an envelope while traveling on
a train to the battlefield.

3. Abigail Adams was the first Second Lady and the
second First Lady of the United States.

4. The first Nobel Peace Prize won by an American
went to Woodrow Wilson in 1921 for his work on The
League of Nations.

5. Mount Rushmore is incomplete, comprising but a
fraction of the original design.

6. The legislation creating the Secret Service was on
Lincoln's desk the night he was shot.

7. Winston Churchill's mother invented the sweet
vermouth and whiskey drink, the "Manhattan."

8. When Fidel Castro came to power in Cuba, he
ordered all Monopoly sets destroyed.

9. Bill Clinton paid his college tuition by performing
with his be-bop group "Willie and the Slick-Tones."

10. In 1947, Chuck Yeager was in the pilot's seat the
first time humans had ever broken the sound barrier.

Answers

1. Hysterical. A well-established myth that has been debunked in recent years, his dentures were made of gold, ivory, lead and human and animal teeth.

2. Hysterical. He was ill, but many copies exist and vary slightly, which showed Lincoln had worked on it for some time.

3. Historical.

4. Hysterical. It was given to Teddy Roosevelt in 1906 for mediating an end to the Russo-Japanese War.

5. Historical. The original concept was for each president to be sculpted from head to waist.

6. Historical.

7. Historical. His mother, Jenny Jerome, was a New York socialite with a knack for concocting cocktails.

8. Historical. If you didn't destroy yours, you went directly to "Jail."

9. Hysterical. Although he plays a mean sax, he went through school on scholarships.

10. Hysterical. Although Yeager was the first human to travel faster than the speed of sound, people had been doing it for thousands of years with whips. The "crack" is a mini-sonic boom as the tip breaks the sound barrier.

World Wide Web of Deceit - Boot Up or Boot Out

Don't believe everything you see on the Internet-
or in this Internet Trivia Quiz. Try to log in to the truth
server by booting up or booting out the following "facts."

1. Netscape Navigator was the first widely-used web browser way back in the 1990s. Boot Up or Boot Out?

2. The original name for Google was "Backrub."

3. The oldest domain name in the world is symbolics.com, which dates from 1985.

4. Floppy disks were developed in the 1970s as a recording medium for music.

5. G-mail originated as a free email service from Garfield the Cat.

6. The first computer trackball was built for the Royal Navy and patented in 1947.

7. The inaugural AOL screen name was registered to investor and Internet champion Al Gore.

8. Before it was Amazon, it was in the books as "Cadabra."

9. A "government handout" of $4 million from the National Science Foundation funded Google's search algorithm.

10. Search engine Bing debuted as "David and Jerry's Guide to the World Wide Web."

Answers

1. Boot Out. It was preceded by Mosaic, released in 1993, which is credited with helping to popularize the Web. Several Mosaic authors went on to develop Navigator.

2. Boot Up. Larry Page and Sergey Brin named it this in 1996. It ultimately became "Google" in 1998.

3. Boot Up. BBN.com came next.

4. Boot Out. Developed in the late 1960s, they were always intended for data storage.

5. Boot Up. The finicky feline's G-mail was bought out by Google and Garfield, as a mail cat, was neutered.

6. Boot Up. It was invented by Ralph Benjamin and later improved on by Canadian Tom Cranston in 1952.

7. Boot Out.

8. Boot Up. Founder Jeff Bezos wanted something that didn't sound quite so much like "cadaver."

9. Boot Up. Google's annual income is now larger than the NSF's entire budget.

10. Boot Out. That would be Yahoo prior to March 1994.

Flush Out The False Fact

They say that two out of three ain't bad...
Your job is to find the bad one in each of the questions.

1. Carrots, celery and cucumbers are three of the vegetable ingredients of V-8 juice.

2. Abigail Adams, Betty Ford and Rosalyn Carter have the same maiden name- Smith.

3. A football goal post, soccer goal post, and basketball rim are all 10 feet high.

4. Athos, Pathos, and Porthos were the Three Musketeers.

5. An "infantacess" is an old name for midwife, a woman hermit was called an "anchoress" and a female lumberjack is a "lumberjill."

6. The Fort Mudge Memorial Dump was a band in the '60s, Willie Billy Beer were southern rockers in the '70s and Liquid Jelly Monkey Love rocked the '90s.

7. A son of Donald Trump's is named Barron, Kanye West's son is North, and Sean Penn's son is South.

8. There are only eight species of bears, jackalopes once wiped out the Texas lettuce crop, and blue whales are pregnant for two years.

9. The Flintstones lived at 222 Rocky Way, the Munsters at 1313 Mockingbird Lane, and George Jetson at 4321 Blastoff Boulevard.

10. The War of 1812 ended in 1824, the 100 Years War lasted 116 years, and The War of the Roses lasted 116 minutes.

Answers

1. Cucumbers are not part of the mix. The others are beats, lettuce, parsley, spinach, tomato and watercress.

2. Betty Ford's maiden name was Bloomer.

3. A soccer goal is 8 feet high.

4. Pathos was not one of the trio. Aramis was the third musketeer.

5. An old name for a midwife is "midwife."

6. Odd band names include The Luminous Toilet Bowls, Ashtray Babyhead and Playdough Fish but, alas, no Willie Billy Beer.

7. Sean Penn's marriage to Robin Wright may have gone that way, but his son's name is not South. It's Hopper.

8. The jackalope's native habitat is in your imagination.

9. George Jetson lived at the Skypad Apartments in Orbit City.

10. The War of 1812 ended in 1814, not 1824. The "War of the Roses," the 1989 black comedy film starring Michael Douglas, Kathleen Turner, and Danny DeVito, did indeed last 116 minutes.

More Dictionary or Fictionary

Test your vocabulary in ten words or less...
no, actually exactly ten words.

1. If this quiz, or another somewhat more stressful situation in your life, gives you butterflies in your stomach, you could be said to be suffering from the "collywobbles." Dictionary or Fictionary?

2. The seat part of playground swings that connects the chains is known as a "slapstrap."

3. Tax instruction manuals, government publications in general and 90% of all speech that emanates from Washington D.C. can be classified as "bafflegab."

4. The aforementioned bureaucratic blather would naturally "bumfuzzle" you.

5. The "!@$#%!" that you sometimes see in comics or cartoons are known as "grawlixes."

6. The perforated grid across the door of a microwave oven is technically a "Gaussonian frequency shield."

7. The division sign "$\div$" is called an "obelus."

8. Your table manners need work if you "bibble," or in other words, eat or drink noisily.

9. The sleeve on the outside of a coffee cup is called a "tweedle."

10. The day after tomorrow has a name. It is called "overmorrow."

Answers

1. Dictionary. The familiar feeling of nervousness is caused by release of adrenaline. It also applies to an upset stomach.

2. Fictionary. They're just called "seats."

3. Dictionary. It was first coined in 1952 by Milton A. Smith.

4. Dictionary. Basically, it means dazed and confused.

5. Dictionary. If you answered Fictionary, maybe you'd feel better if you just go @#&%%@!

6. Fictionary. The mesh is a sort of reverse Faraday cage to keep the microwaves from leaking out.

7. Dictionary.

8. Dictionary. The only thing less polite is to dribble while you bibble.

9. Fictionary. Actually, it's called a zarf.

10. Dictionary.

Truths of the Throne

The highest bathrooms in the western hemisphere are in the Willis Tower, formerly the Sears Tower, in Chicago.

Find the Flush Factor

Three of the following "facts" are, in fact, fallacies. Flush them from the aforementioned factual factoids.

1. Russia actually had a "Doomsday Machine" as portrayed in the cold war classic "Dr. Strangelove."

2. Costumed characters working Disney World in the summer have a special flap in their costumes that holds a block of dry ice to keep them cool when temperatures soar above 90.

3. The Sahara is the largest desert in the world.

4. The first video game was invented to test the intelligence of monkeys.

5. If your DIY project requires a square hole, you can make one with an ordinary hand-held rotary drill.

6. San Francisco has an ordinance against picking up and throwing used confetti.

7. Affirmed was the last Triple Crown winner in horse racing in 1978.

8. The little tips that bind up the ends of your shoelaces are called "aglets."

9. The Pentagon has incontrovertible, definitive proof that UFOs exist.

10. Mayim Bialik not only plays a neuroscientist on "The Big Bang Theory," she holds a neuroscience Ph.D. in real life.

Answers

1. Fact. Called the "Dead Hand System," it could react automatically to certain conditions and events and independently launch a nuclear strike.

2. Flush. They switch out characters often so that they don't spend too much time in costume. They also use small fans and are developing water-cooled costumes.

3. Flush. Antarctica is a desert that is over two million square miles greater in extent than the Sahara.

4. Flush. The very first primitive game in 1947 was called "Cathode Ray Tube Amusement Device", based on WW2 radar screens. "Computer Space" and "Pong" came along in the 1970s and merely tested the quarter supply of the humans playing them.

5. Fact. There are workarounds but the simple and easiest way is with a Watts drill based on the Reuleaux triangle. As it turns, it actually makes a square hole. A similar drill bit can make hexagonal holes.

6. Fact. Used glitter bombs on the other hand...

7. Fact.

8. Fact. And just so you know, if they are purely decorative, they are known as aiguillettes.

9. Fact. Unidentified Flying Objects are seen and documented all the time. Whether or not they are alien flying saucers is an entirely different debate.

10. Fact. At UCLA, she triple majored in Hebrew and Jewish Studies along with neuroscience.

Product Fact or Flush

How well do you know the products that you use every day?
Let's find out if you're one smart customer or
if your opinion should just be discounted.

1. Maxwell House Coffee was given its slogan by
Teddy Roosevelt.

2. Kitty litter tends to be radioactive.

3. The words "Coca Cola" in Chinese translate roughly
to "bite the wax tadpole."

4. Canola oil is produced by tapping the Canola tree
which is common throughout Mexico.

5. Ikea makes a high chair for dogs.

6. Motorola got its name from the name of its first
wildly successful product, a car radio.

7. Dr Pepper has no period in its name.

8. The Nintendo Cereal System was released in 1988
featuring a breakfast cereal containing characters from
Super Mario Brothers and Legend of Zelda.

9. Wheaties, Bisquick and Green Giant vegetables
were all created in Minnesota.

10. Eggos debuted with the name "Froffles."

Answers

1. Fact. When asked how he liked it, Teddy enthusiastically replied "It was good to the last drop," and that's been the slogan ever since.

2. Fact. Bentonite, one of the types of clay used in litter, is high in uranium and thorium. If your cat box is about to go nuclear, time to change it.

3. Fact. Depending on your pronunciation it can also sound like "female horse stuffed with wax." Either one sure sounds refreshing.

4. Flush. It is a type of rapeseed oil. It was given a more market-friendly name and as it was grown mainly in Canada, it was branded Canola.

5. Flush. The "Hundstol" highchair with a hole in the back for tails and built in food and water bowls was a hoax launched by Ikea on April 1st.

6. Fact. It started out as the Galvin manufacturing company.

7. Fact.

8. Fact. It was manufactured by Ralston and now sells for about $100 a box at memorabilia auctions.

9. Fact. Minnesota is also the home of Scotch Tape and HMO's (well, you can't win them all).

10. Fact. The named was changed after customers consistently described them as "eggy."

Multiple Choice Fact or Flush

Extract the fact from the flushables.

1. The first U.S. president born in a hospital was:
    a) Eisenhower   b) Carter   c) Hoover

2. A "pomato" is a hybrid of: a) potato/tomato
    b) pomegranate/potato   c) pomegranate/tomato

3. The oldest gun company in the world is:
          a) Colt   b) Enfield   c) Beretta

4. The first cover of "People" magazine featured:
    a) Tom Selleck   b) Mia Farrow   c) David Hasselhoff

5. You've just driven through Possumneck, Hot Coffee
and Chunky. Therefore you are visiting:
        a) Georgia   b) West Virginia   c) Mississippi

6. In 1962, the "Galactic Network" was first conceived
and we know it now as:
    a) The Internet   b) On Star   c) Sirius Radio XM

7. In 1953, the first one of these opened in
Jacksonville, Florida.
        a) McDonalds   b) Subway   c) Burger King

8. Jerome Lester Horwitz is better known and beloved
to Baby Boomers and Beyonders as:
a) Ringo Starr b) Curly (Three Stooges) c) Soupy Sales

9. The first novel written entirely on a typewriter was:
a)"Tom Sawyer" b)"Nostromo" c)"The Great Gatsby"

10. Tiger Woods' first name is:
            a) Ernest   b) Elrod   c) Eldrick

Answers

1. Fact B.

2. Fact A. The others would be just plain yuck!

3. Fact C. They've been hiring and firing since they were established in 1526 in Brescia, Italy.

4. Fact B.

5. Fact C.

6. Fact A.

7. Fact C. Back then, it was called "Insta-Burger."

8. Fact B.

9. Fact A. Mark Twain always loved the latest technology.

10. Fact C.

Truths of the Throne

The Union ironclad Monitor was the first US ship equipped with a flush toilet. Guess it was just a "head" of its time.

Lifestyles of the Rich and/or Famous Fact or Flush

Can you tell the fab from the fabrication?
Thumbs up or Thumbs down, it's your call…

1. Florian Cloud de Bounevialle O'Malley Armstrong is better known as Dido.

2. Jake Gyllenhaal was given his first driving lesson by Paul Newman.

3. Before he really clicked and could write his own ticket, Johnny Depp supported himself by selling pens.

4. John Stamos, best known for the long-running comedy "Full House," is a recurring member of the Beach Boys.

5. Jennifer Garner's uncle is James Garner, famous for his roles as Brett Maverick and Jim Rockford.

6. Tom Hanks collects typewriters from the 1940s.

7. Amanda Lee Rogers chucked her plain-Jane name for her new marquee moniker, Portia De Rossi.

8. After he was drafted, Elvis trained as a fighter pilot.

9. Despite a glitzy, glamorous life, Nicole Kidman is still haunted by lepidopterophobia.

10. Queen Elizabeth joined both Facebook and Twitter.

Answers

1. Fact. That mouthful of a moniker may have been better suited for her previous profession- literary agent.

2. Fact.

3. Fact. He sold pens on the phone and hated it. When the supervisor was out of earshot, Depp would whisper to his client, "Don't buy this pen," explaining that they were thieves and the company's promotions were crooked.

4. Fact. He may not be a permanent full time member, but he has played with them many, many times.

5. Flush. They are not related. James Garner's birth name was James Scott Bumgarner.

6. Fact. In fact, he uses one almost every day.

7. Fact.

8. Flush. Although he was offered special preferential treatment by both the Army and the Navy, Elvis opted to be just a regular old G.I. serving in Germany.

9. Fact. She has a terrible fear of butterflies.

10. Fact. Of course, it's not possible to poke the Royal family- and the royals have all their tweeting done by servants. (Royal Twits, perhaps?)

Your Tax Dollars at Shirk
Fact or Flush

Whether you like big government or small, nobody
likes red tape. It seems if they're not taxing your
income, they're taxing your patience.
Check out this list of grievances and choose
which ones you can support...

1. To protect children from controversial language, a
California school board once banned the dictionary.

2. Planning to take Fido to France, Fiji or some other
faraway place? Then he needs a passport as well.

3. The Postal Service once fired a missile from a
submarine to test their new speedy delivery system.

4. Due to an act of Congress, pizza is a vegetable.

5. In the 1960's, the FBI launched an investigation
into the lyrics of "Louie Louie" by the Kingsmen.

6. NASA's spending $3 million through 2017 to study
Congress.

7. The Federal Highway Administration has mandated
that all street signs contain upper and lowercase letters.

8. It's not just our government. French authorities just
ordered billions of dollars of trains that are too wide to
fit in their stations.

9. Reef divers in the Florida Keys must wear blue scuba
tanks so as to not upset fish or other coral dwellers.

10. Due to an oversight, Mississippi didn't officially
ratify the 13th Amendment, outlawing slavery, until
2013.

Answers

1. Fact. The decision was later reversed after the voters had some controversial words with them.

2. Flush. Not a passport per se but a ream of other documents.

3. Fact. Back in 1959, a sub off Florida launched a missile at the mainland and successfully delivered the mail. Due to expense and Cold War concerns, the idea was eventually shot down.

4. Flush. But close! They declared pizza sauce should count as a vegetable.

5. Fact. It took around a year to determine that the lyrics were officially unintelligible.

6. Fact. Yes, Congress. So much for their search for intelligent life! Guess they've had enough of the Right Stuff and are now looking for the Wrong Stuff.

7. Fact. Phoenix, for example, which has all its street signs in capital letters, now will have to lay out about $11 million to correct their signage.

8. Fact. Now they are spending millions more to widen the station platforms.

9. Flush. The spear guns probably clash much worse, anyhow.

10. Fact. It was a relatively minor clerical error, but what is unbelievable is that they waited until 1995 to do anything about it at all. That was 130 years after most states accepted the Amendment!

Little Known Facts About Well Known People Fact or Flush

Sure, you recognize the names, but
how well do you know them as people?
Which facts are bona fide and which are just bluffs?

1. British naturalist and broadcaster David Attenborough can also take credit for putting "Monty Python's Flying Circus" on television.

2. Jason Sudekis' uncle is George Wendt, "Norm" from "Cheers."

3. Chuck Berry originally studied to be a hairdresser before being groomed for a music career.

4. Before becoming Xena Warrior Princess, Lucy Lawless wore the crown of Miss New Zealand.

5. According to Forbes, J.K. Rowling was the only person ever to become a billionaire from writing books.

6. "The Daily Show's" Jon Stewart was a Yugo salesman in the 1980s.

7. James Doohan, "Scotty" from the original "Star Trek" TV series, was shot six times on D-Day.

8. Al Gore has been known to hypnotize chickens.

9. The late, great comedian John Candy was on the 1976 Canadian Olympic curling team.

10. In college, Hillary Clinton was president of the Young Republicans Club.

Answers

1. Fact. He commissioned the program for BBC 2 in the late 1960s.

2. Fact. George is his mother's brother.

3. Fact. He went from "duck tails" to the "duck walk."

4. Fact. She was crowned in 1989.

5. Fact. Although due to high taxes and massive donations to charity, she's no longer in the billionaire's club.

6. Flush. But he was a soccer coach, bartender and shelf stocker before going into comedy.

7. Fact.

8. Fact. Other chicken hypnotists include Adam Savage and Will Smith.

9. Flush. Candy did have a Canadian sports connection though. He was part owner with Wayne Gretzky of the Canadian Football League's Toronto Argonauts.

10. Fact.

Truths of the Throne

A whopping 75% of people use their mobile phone to text, phone and surf the web while they're in the bathroom.

Off the Shelf Fact or Flush

Name brand facts or just branded as a lie?

1. Snapple was named after its very first flavor of spice and apple.

2. The name for that tiny strip of paper in each Hershey's Kiss is a "Higgalty-Piggalty."

3. Sprite started out as Clear Lemon Fanta in Germany.

4. Hydrox cookies were an attempt to cash in on the runaway success of Oreos.

5. Kit Kats in Japan can be made with alcohol.

6. Pop Rocks were invented in 1957 but not sold until 1975 because of the relatively short shelf life.

7. Even though they never even contained the ingredient, red M&Ms were discontinued in the 1970s due to Red Dye #2 safety concerns.

8. Marshmallow chicks are sold on North Korea's black market much like drugs are in the US.

9. If you parachute with a can of spray cheese, it is likely to explode and may cause the edges of the chute to stick together, preventing deployment.

10. The venerable candy bar Snickers was named after the Mars family horse.

Answers

1. Fact. Good thing the first flavor wasn't cranberry-apple.

2. Flush. Its proper name is the "Niggly Wiggly."

3. Fact. It was brought to the United States in 1961 to compete with 7-Up. By the way, "Fanta" means "imagination" in German.

4. Flush. Hydrox came first. It debuted in 1908 while Oreo was a comparative Johnny-come-lately in 1912. Kelloggs, which had acquired the brand by the early 2000s, quietly killed off the cookie just after its 100th birthday.

5. Fact. Other flavors include creamy green tea filling and blueberry fromage.

6. Fact. They are manufactured under 600 lb. per square inch pressure of carbon dioxide and tend to go "flat."

7. Fact. They were phased back in 10 years later.

8. Flush. The Peep Police would probably catch you anyway.

9. Flush. And what are the odds of this being discovered in any case?

10. Fact. Globally, they sell about $2 billion a year of them. That's one horse bet that paid off big time!

Brain Drain

Ten random "facts" to either file in your
brain or send down the drain...

1. The Nazis had a hidden base in North America that wasn't discovered until 1977. Brain or Drain?

2. The hole that allows you to put the straw through the cup's cap and into the drink is called a "spurdle."

3. An underwater restaurant in the Bahamas has a drive-thru window for mini-subs.

4. Cleopatra loved smoking dried asparagus spears.

5. It is illegal to enter Parliament while wearing a suit of armor.

6. By Swedish law, an ice hotel, rebuilt every year from blocks hewn from a frozen river, must have a fire alarm system.

7. There's a crater on the Moon named "Beer."

8. Babe Ruth's first name was Rudolph.

9. Florence Nightingale was the inventor of the pie chart.

10. "The Guinness Book of World Records" is in itself as the record holder for the book most stolen from libraries.

Answers

1. Brain. The locals knew about it but no one believed them for a long time.

2. Brain. That's just what it's called.

3. Drain. Now there's a drive-up speaker that would REALLY be hard to understand!

4. Drain. People used to tell her, "Those asps are going to kill you!"

5. Brain. It is also considered a bit of a cheek if you expire in Parliament- you wouldn't be invited back that's for sure.

6. Brain. Although during a fire, you wouldn't need an alarm so much as a snorkel.

7. Brain. There is also a crater on Mars named "Beer," named after astronomer Wilhelm Beer. Wonder if there's a comet Ale-Bopp?

8. Drain. He was born George Herman Ruth.

9. Brain. It was the type now called the circular histogram.

10. Brain.

Truths of the Throne

November 19 is World Toilet Day. Considering the time of year, some call it "Tanksgiving."

Pot Luck
Fact or Flush

1. There is no latitude on the globe where you could sail completely around the world in an east-west direction and not run into land.

2. If you called a Dominos in India, you could order a pizza with minced mutton, pickled ginger and tofu.

3. Storing batteries in the freezer recharges them.

4. In "The Wizard of Oz," the story was driven by a fearful Gale.

5. More tigers are owned by private citizens in the US than live in the wild worldwide.

6. The device used to detect and measure nuclear explosions from space is called a "Bhangmeter."

7. European bowling pins and balls are made of rubber to provide the game with more action and excitement.

8. Bermuda is closer to New York than it is to Florida.

9. In the U.S., dogs make more popular pets than cats by a wide margin.

10. That classic dramatic sting "Dun Dun DUN!", which has become synonymous with suspense, is known by the simple title, "Shock Horror (a)."

Answers

1. Flush. Down around 60° south latitude you could circumnavigate the globe without striking land.

2. Fact. Although ordering from the US, you probably couldn't get it delivered in 30 minutes or less.

3. Flush. However, storing nicad batteries in the freezer has been reported to extend their lives by 90%.

4. Fact. Dorothy's last name is "Gale" and she found those flying monkeys pretty scary.

5. Fact. The six subspecies are all classified as "endangered." Only somewhat over 3,000 remain in the wild.

6. Fact.

7. Flush.

8. Fact. Being off the Carolinas, "tropical" Bermuda is much more northerly than most people think.

9. Flush. Not if you go strictly by numbers. It's 96 million cats vs. 83 million dogs. How many of those cats are simply holding their human hostage isn't known.

10. Fact. It was written by British composer Dick Walter.

Find The Flush Factor

Delete the duo of deceptions.

1. Colorado is the only state in history to turn down the Winter Olympics.

2. Cleopatra lived closer in time to the moon landing than to the construction of the Great Pyramid at Giza.

3. If you play an old 45 RPM record too many times, it wears out and begins playing the flip side backwards. Among DJs, this was known as "Top 40 radio burn."

4. George W. Bush was the first Little League baseball player to become President of the United States.

5. There's an online dating service that matches people up by their credit scores.

6. The real reason museums don't allow flash photography is that with today's technology of 3-D and laser printing, a really sharp, clear photo could be turned into a forgery.

7. Spain requires drivers to always carry a spare- a spare set of glasses that is.

8. China retains ownership of all pandas. They are only rented out to zoos.

9. Pope Francis holds a master's degree in chemistry from the University of Buenos Aires.

10. The ancient Greeks had no word or concept for the color blue.

Answers

1. Fact. Voters decided that it wasn't worth the trouble back in the mid 70s.

2. Fact. The Great Pyramid at Giza is dated at 2584 BC, Cleopatra was born 69 BC, and the moon landing was in 1969.

3. Flush. Radio records however did get "cue scratches" from racking them up to play.

4. Fact.

5. Fact. Obviously it's for lovers looking to get a charge out of each other.

6. Flush. Paintings, in particular, have a "light life." Light actually degrades the artwork, especially bright, intense light. As they want to keep them looking good for centuries, no flash photography please.

7. Fact. If you are among the vision-impaired, extra specs cut down on extra wrecks.

8. Fact. The going rate is $1 million a year and the panda is guaranteed a 10-year minimum gig.

9. Fact.

10. Fact. Homer described the sky as "bronze."

The Body Odd Fact or Flush

You should know your body pretty well. After all, you've lived there all your life. Here, some fascinating facts have been fleshed out with some fantastic fibs...

1. Maybe it's your best friend who should tell you this, but you have a glabella right in the middle of you face.

2. If you have curly hair, it means your follicles are flat.

3. When you're doing jumping jacks, you are actually pandiculating.

4. The average person blinks about 8 million times a year.

5. Algophobia is an abnormal fear of bodily infection that can be caused by drinking well water containing algae.

6. Your brain has a higher percentage of water than a watermelon does.

7. The fastest growing nail is on your middle finger.

8. It's a common misconception that a dog's sense of smell is better than a human's.

9. The appendix serves absolutely no purpose other than to give people appendicitis.

10. Goose bumps are evolution's attempt to make us look bigger.

Answers

1. Fact. It's the space between your eyebrows, just above your nose.

2. Fact. Round follicles grow straight hair.

3. Flush. Pandiculating is the act of stretching and yawning. Of course, if that's your way of exercising, then we stand corrected.

4. Fact.

5. Flush. Algophobia is a fear of pain.

6. Flush. The brain is about 80% water while a watermelon's H_2O content is 93%.

7. Fact. And it's on the middle finger of the dominant hand that it grows fastest.

8. Flush. Dogs' smellers are about 20 times more acute than ours.

9. Flush. It functions as a place for your gut bacteria to breed and get some R&R. Healthy bacteria usually helps your digestive system stay healthy.

10. Fact. Mammals fluff up their body hair in response to cold and fear. This can make them appear larger to a potential enemy. Unfortunately, with the sparse body hair of a human, all it succeeds in doing is making us look like a plucked chicken.

Kid's Stuff Fact or Flush

Are we playing it straight or just kidding around?

1. Candy corn was invented by a disgruntled employee of Hershey's, who started his own company when management refused to sell his seasonal confection.

2. Hopscotch originated as part of the Marine basic training obstacle course to test coordination and balance in 1907.

3. All Gummy bears were imported prior to 1982.

4. Nintendo tried to market the game of Twister to Japan without success.

5. Over 5 billion little green houses have been produced for Monopoly since the game's introduction in 1935.

6. Fruit Stripe Gum's zebra mascot is named Yipes.

7. The Obamas named "Bo," their first Portuguese Water Dog, after the dog which appears on the box of Cracker Jack.

8. When Franken Berry cereal debuted in 1971, many children were rushed to the hospital with a condition that came to be known as "Franken Berry Stool."

9. The game of "Life" has been banned as blasphemy by several religious sects in the USA as recently as 2012.

10. Antarctic explorer Admiral Byrd took 2 1/2 tons of Necco Wafers with him to the South Pole on a two year expedition.

Answers

1. Flush. It was invented by George Renninger in the 1880s. It went into wider production around 1900.

2. Flush. The game dates back to Roman times.

3. Fact. They originated as "The Dancing Bears" in Germany. A domestic factory finally opened in Baltimore, Maryland, in 1982.

4. Fact. It never caught on since, at the time, it was considered improper for boys and girls to be in such close proximity.

5. Fact. Considering how many must be in landfills by now, there're a lot of very happy ants with their own private condos.

6. Fact. There have been other characters over the years but they haven't had the sticking power of Yipes.

7. Flush. The dog's name on the box of Cracker Jack is Bingo.

8. Fact. The garish pink dye used wasn't absorbed and came out the same color that it went in, causing a panic among parents. The offending dye has long since been removed.

9. Flush.

10. Fact. They were brought to sustain his men during the expedition and afterwards, their dentists once they got home.

Flush Out The False Fact

Rev up your personal polygraph and
flush out the falsehood in each question.

1. Americans were the first to reach the moon, it takes
over 8 minutes for the sun's light to reach us, and
milk has been discovered in the Milky Way Galaxy.

2. The Buffalo Bills, Minnesota Vikings, and New York
Jets have all been to, but never won, the Super Bowl.

3. Gelotology is the study of humor, osmics is the
study of smells and batology is the science of bats.

4. The "WD" in WD-40 is for its inventor, Wayne
Devers, "J&B" scotch stands for Justerini and Brooks
and BMW stands for Bavarian Motor Works.

5. Jimi Hendrix, Janis Joplin and Buddy Holly were
all 27 when they died.

6. There are no naturally green mammals, rats can
swim from the sewer to the toilet bowl, and cats don't
have belly buttons.

7. Mick Jagger studied to be an accountant, Dick
Cheney once won the National Quick Draw
Championship, and Warren Beatty was a rat catcher.

8. Paul Simon, Daniel Radcliffe, and Ryan Seacrest are
all under 5'6."

9. Robert Downey Jr. broke Halle Berry's arm, John
Goodman broke Tom Arnold's jaw and Robin Williams
broke Robert De Niro's nose.

10. Babe Ruth played for the New York Yankees,
Boston Red Sox, and Brooklyn Dodgers.

Answers

1. America was not first. In 1959, the Soviet Union launched Luna 2, the first spacecraft to reach the Moon. And by the way, there is actual milk in the Milky Way. We have milk and we are in the Milky Way.

2. Not true about the Jets- Yes, they've each been to the big game, but New York did win once, in 1969.

3. "Batology" has been falsified here. It is the branch of botany which studies brambles.

4. "WD-40" stands for "Water displacement, 40th formula."

5. Buddy Holly was only 22 the day his music died.

6. Cats do have belly buttons. They are a small scar on the underside.

7. Jagger went to The London School of Economics and Beatty did the Pied Piper thing. Cheney didn't do his thing.

8. Seacrest stands out at 5'8". Radcliffe's height is 5'5" and Simon is 5'3".

9. Downey accidentally broke Berry's arm while filming "Gothika" and Robin Williams accidentally broke De Niro's nose while making "Insomnia." That Goodman-Arnold jaw thing never happened.

10. The Babe never played for the Dodgers, but he did play for the Pirates as well as Yanks and Sox.

Underneath It All Fact or Flush

Try these fashion statements on for size.

1. The word "wedgie" comes from "wedge-heeled shoe" and became popular in the 1970s from the effect it gave the victim.

2. Roy Raymond invented the thong in 1977.

3. Women in Italy celebrate the New Year by wearing red underwear because it is considered lucky.

4. In 1951, Marlon Brando helped turn men's cotton undershirts into outerwear when he wore an undershirt in the movie "A Streetcar Named Desire."

5. "Long Johns" were originally worn by bare-knuckled boxer John L. Sullivan in the late 1800s.

6. In 2012, Zimbabwe banned the importation and sale of second-hand underwear.

7. The average American woman owns approximately 30 pairs of underwear.

8. In 1913, Mary Phelps Jacob took two silk handkerchiefs and tied them together with a pink ribbon, thus creating the first brassiere.

9. BVD, as in underwear, stands for the manufacturers names, Bradley, Voorhees and Day.

10. Umar Farouk Abdulmutallab introduced underwear to Nigeria in 1976, where natives went commando before his import of the product.

Answers

1. Fact.

2. Flush. Raymond started the Victoria's Secret chain that year in San Francisco.

3. Fact.

4. Fact.

5. Fact. He wore long woolen drawers while boxing in cold weather.

6. Fact. Authorities hope the ban will aid health concerns and help the country's own domestic textile industry.

7. Flush. The average woman has 21 pairs of underwear- and 10% own over 35 pairs.

8. Fact.

9. Fact.

10. Flush. Abdulmutallab is known as the "Underwear Bomber," who unsuccessfully attempted to detonate explosives in his underpants on a Detroit-bound airplane on Christmas Day in 2009.

Truths of the Throne

In the 1930s, the Addis Brush Company created the first artificial brush trees for Christmas using the same machinery which made their toilet brushes.

Fowl Play Fact or Flush

See if you can detect the fowl
statements in this bird fare.

1. Colonel Sanders, the founder of Kentucky Fried Chicken, was born in Indiana.

2. Donald Duck's nephews were Huey, Dewey, and Louie and his nieces were Dolly, Polly, and Molly.

3. The middle name of The Donald (Duck, that is) is Fauntleroy.

4. A group of geese is called a gander.

5. Benjamin Franklin proposed that the turkey be the symbol of the United States rather than the eagle.

6. Ducks have three eyelids.

7. The name of the rooster on the Kellogg's Corn Flakes box is Cornelius.

8. A raw egg spins more easily than a hard-boiled one.

9. Those flaps of flesh that dangle under a rooster's chin are called jangles.

10. Chickens are color-blind.

Answers

1. Fact.

2. Flush. The nephews' names are okay, but the nieces were April, May, and June.

3. Fact.

4. Flush. It's a gaggle.

5. Fact.

6. Fact.

7. Fact.

8. Flush. The moving liquids in a raw egg cause it to wobble.

9. Flush. They are called wattles.

10. Flush. They see in full color.

Truths of the Throne

Americans use 433 million miles of toilet paper a year. That's enough to stretch to the sun and back.

Find The Flush Factor

In a quiz book full of deceit, this is the most deceitful. Can you separate the four bonafide facts from the six bogus ones?

1. The movie "Titanic" cost almost thirty times as much as the real Titanic.

2. Almost every pigeon you've ever seen is female as the much smaller males die soon after mating.

3. "Lachanophobia" is the fear of vegetables.

4. The first owner of a professional sports franchise to host "Saturday Night Live" was Mark Cuban of the NBA's Dallas Mavericks.

5. Solar system and interstellar space explorer Voyager 1 has a Twitter account.

6. A person with deuteranopia has trouble keeping balanced.

7. The NFL takes in almost $10 billion a year and yet is exempt from taxes.

8. Elvis "The King of Rock and Roll" Presley never won a Grammy for any of his hip-swiveling rock recordings.

9. "Sports Illustrated's Swimsuit Edition" is banned in Spain.

10. The celebrated Golden Spike which linked up the railroads from the East and West in Promontory, Utah, in 1869, was stolen before the festivities even ended.

Answers

1. Fact. Ship construction was about $7 million while the movie came in at around $200 million.

2. Flush. And where are all the baby pigeons? Well, they stay in the nest in out-of-the-way places until they are ready for pigeon prime time.

3. Fact.

4. Flush. It was George Steinbrenner, on October 20, 1990.

5. Flush. However, the Mars rover Curiosity does-@MarsCuriosity.

6. Flush. Deuteranopia is red-green color blindness.

7. Fact. It is considered a non-profit organization.

8. Fact. All three of his wins were in the Gospel category. It didn't help that the Grammys only began in 1958, when Elvis was in the Army in Germany.

9. Flush. It does offend some subscribers, though. Upon request, the magazine will skip sending the edition out and extend the subscription by one week.

10. Flush. Knowing that it would be purloined if left there, they removed it immediately and it is now safely on display at the Cantor Arts Museum at Stanford University.

On the Ball Fact or Flush

See if you can determine whether
these questions take a true bounce or not.

1. A football's shape is known as a prolate spheroid.

2. There are more keys on a piano than there are
stitches on an official baseball.

3. When the very first game of basketball was played in
1892, a volleyball was used to toss into peach baskets
at either end of the court.

4. A golden retriever named Augie from Dallas, Texas,
owns the doggie world record for holding the most
tennis balls in the mouth at one time- 5.

5. The cue ball in pool was originally green but
conflicted with the color of the table so it was switched
to white and the previously white 6-ball became green.

6. K.C. Chiefs team owner Lamar Hunt thought of the
name Super Bowl from watching his kids play with a
Super Ball.

7. The yellow colored tennis ball was introduced in
1972 as "Optic Yellow" after research showed it was
the easiest color to be seen on color TV.

8. Before the 20th century, soccer players were at the
mercy of the size and shape of the pig's bladder which
was used as the game "ball."

9. Volleyball was originally called badminton.

10. The street game of stickball features a rubber ball
often called a "Spaldeen," a term from the New York-
accented pronunciation of the manufacturer, Spalding.

Answers

1. Fact.

2. Flush. There are 108 stitches on a baseball and 88 keys on a piano.

3. Flush- James Naismith, the game's inventor, used a soccer ball.

4. Fact.

5. Flush.

6. Fact.

7. Fact. Before then, most balls were colored white.

8. Fact. Charles Goodyear created the first vulcanized rubber soccer ball in 1855.

9. Flush. It was called Mintonette when William G. Morgan invented it in 1895.

10. Fact.

Truths of the Throne

The toilet is flushed more times during Super Bowl halftime than at any time during the year.